36 STRATAGEMS

三十六计

Secret Art Of War

ASIAPAC COMIC SERIES

● STRATEGY & LEADERSHIP ●

36 STRATAGEMS
三十六计
Secret Art Of War

Edited & illustrated by Wang Xuanming

Translated by
Koh Kok Kiang (comics)
and Liu Yi (texts of the stratagems)

ASIAPAC · SINGAPORE

Publisher
ASIAPAC BOOKS PTE LTD
996 Bendemeer Road #06-08/09
Kallang Basin Industrial Estate
Singapore 339944
Tel: (65) 392 8455
Fax: (65) 392 6455
Email apacbks@singnet.com.sg

Come visit us at our Internet home page:
www.asiapacbooks.com

First published Sep 1992
Revised edition Jan 1993
Reprinted Jul 1993, Feb 1994, Feb 1995,
        Mar 1996, Apr 1998

© 1992 ASIAPAC BOOKS, SINGAPORE
ISBN 9971-985-94-2

Cover design by Roy Tan
Typeset by Quaser Technology Private Limited
Printed in Singapore by Loi Printing Pte Ltd

Publisher's Note

Comics play an important role in our fast-moving urban society. They serve the young as well as the adult readers. Comics are fun and entertaining. They can also be a kind of satire and can even make classical literature and philosophy available to us in a light-hearted way.

We are pleased to present the work of Wang Xuanming, a contemporary cartoonist from Mainland China, who has illustrated a series of ancient Chinese military classics into comics. Mr Koh Kok Kiang has translated the first of the five books in this series.

We would like to thank Mr Liu Yi, a translator from Mainland China, for his translation of the classical texts of the 36 stratagems. We have included his translation into Wang Xuanming's comics and this has greatly enriched our present edition of *The 36 Stratagems*.

We feel honoured to have the cartoonist Wang Xuanming's permission to the translation rights to his best selling comics. We would also like to thank the translators, especially Mr Koh Kok Kiang, for writing the Foreword, and the production team for putting in their best effort in the production of this series.

Titles in the Strategy & Leadership Series

Thirty-six Stratagems
Six Strategies for War
Gems of Chinese Wisdom
Three Strategies of Huang Shi Gong
100 Strategies of War
Sixteen Strategies of Zhuge Liang
Sunzi's Art of War

About the Editor/Illustrator

Wang Xuanming, a contemporary cartoonist in China, was born in Beijing in 1950. He was trained formally in commercial art and industrial art. Since 1972, he has been engaged in various aspects of artistic work, even undertaking the production of screen advertisements and artistic stage designs. Wang's contribution to the field of art is immense. He frequently explores various ways of expressing his artistic talents. Besides a lot of cartoons, picture books, and illustrations, he also does oil paintings and posters. His works have on many occasions entered the nationwide art exhibition, won awards in several art competitions, and have been selected for inclusion in various art albums.

Wang's cartoons, illustrations and other works have been serialized in all the major newspapers and publications in Beijing since 1980. His cartoons entitled *Different Gravitational Force* was praised by famous Chinese artists, and was selected for inclusion in the *Anthology of Chinese Scientific Cartoons*. In 1987, he participated in the creation of the animated cartoon *Brother Elephant,* which captured the hearts of many children when it was first shown on television.

Wang has worked with many publishers in Beijing, such as China Friendly Publishing Co., Chinese Cultural Publishing Co., Huaxia Publishing Co., People's Art Publishing Co., and Zhaohua Publishing Co. He has gained the trust and confidence of both publishers and artists alike.

In his latest comic series, Books of Strategy, he uses a simple and humorous art form to introduce the ancient Chinese military classics to the modern readers. The books were very well received by people from all walks of life when they were first published in China; the Beijing Radio Station made a special interview of this series of books and highly recommended it to the public. This series is published by China Friendly Publishing Co. in China, and by Treasure Creation Co. Ltd. in Hongkong. Asiapac Books in Singapore is the publisher for the English edition of this series.

Wang is at present an art editor at the *China Science and Technology Daily.*

Foreword

Until recently, not many people may have read the book *The 36 Stratagems*. But they certainly would have come across the saying: "Of the 36 stratagems, running away is the best option", or "Lure the tiger out of the mountain". The popular saying, "Of the 36 stratagems, running away is the best option", first appeared in the official history of Southern Qi about 1,500 years ago. Since then, it has gained increasing currency.

About 300 years ago, either towards the end of the Ming Dynasty or the beginning of the Qing Dynasty, an unknown scholar decided to compile all the 36 stratagems into a small book called *Secret Art of War: The 36 Stratagems*. It initially only circulated and survived in handwritten copies. It was first published in 1941 by the Xinghua Printing House in Chengdu, Sichuan. Since then several editions have appeared in Chinese and other East Asian languages.

The 36 Stratagems stands out among the military classics of ancient China for its emphasis on deception as a military art; most other military classics are about battlefield tactics. Unlike many books of its genre, *The 36 Stratagems* focuses on the use of deception, subterfuge or hidden tactics to achieve military objectives. Hence its title, *Secret Art of War: The 36 Stratagems*.

Apart from a preface and an afterword, the book falls into six sections of six stratagems each. There is a brief text with a quotation from the *Yi Jing* (the Book of Changes), the most revered classic of China, and a comment on the strategy.

The 36 Stratagems was composed in conformity to the yin-yang doctrine formulated in the Book of Changes. Yin and yang are two complementary qualities in the universe and everything in the world is thought to belong to one or the other. Yin, the female element, is associated with the dark and hidden while Yang, the male element, is associated with light and openness. The ancient Chinese regarded ploys and stratagems, often hatched and carried out in secrecy, to belong to the yin. Yin in the Book of Changes is represented by the hexagram for earth which is composed of six lines, with each line broken into segments, resulting in two columns of six short lines, whose product is 36.

In the book, sometimes the name of the stratagem refers directly to a famous incident in history in which the stratagem was first used, such as "Besiege Wei to rescue Zhao". The text of the stratagem is very brief – the shortest being nine Chinese characters and the longest, 32 characters. It is so condensed that one can interpret it according to one's own understanding.

The 36 stratagems are grouped into six sets; the first three are designed for use when one holds the advantage, and the second three when one is at a disadvantage. They are: stratagems when commanding superiority, stratagems for confrontation, stratagems for attack, stratagems for confusing situations, stratagems for gaining ground, and stratagems for desperate situations.

This categorisation, however, was never meant to be rigid. On the contrary, several millennia of practising and refining battle tactics have taught the Chinese military strategists that the highest principle of all was flexibility.

In most modern books on the 36 stratagems, examples from the many battles of ancient China are given on the application of the stratagems. The examples show the ingenuity, folly, bravery and even calculated brutality of the Chinese in warfare. Although the examples of the use of the stratagems are drawn from Chinese history, there is no doubt that their application can be universal as human nature is basically the same everywhere. War is a human activity, therefore it follows certain patterns which are a projection of human nature. As long as human nature does not change, war will continue to follow certain patterns which can be observed by a discerning mind.

Nevertheless, it may be argued that many of the stratagems are no longer applicable in today's hi-tech world where technological superiority and sheer firepower would outweigh other factors. But is this really the case?

A notable example of the successful use of a stratagem is the recent Gulf War between Iraq and the multinational allied forces led by the United States.

Iraq had annexed Kuwait and that led to the international campaign to liberate Kuwait. At first, the allies used massive air strikes and missile blasts in the hope of pounding the Iraqis into submission and thereby avoiding a bloody land war and hand-to-hand combat. But the Iraqis refused to yield despite being subjected to "seeing eye" computer-guided precision bombing designed to inflict maximum damage on military targets. Finally, when it became clear that the time had come for a decisive land war, the allies resorted to using a stratagem to end the agony as soon as possible and to avoid heavy loss of life. General

Norman Schwarzkopf, commander of the allied forces, imposed a news blackout while his military strategy was being implemented. If it were not a "hidden art", why was the news blackout necessary?

As it turned out, the allied forces applied the strategy of "making a feint to the east while attacking in the west" (Stratagem 6). The allies had been practising amphibious landings and the Iraqis were led to believe that the main invasion would come by sea via Kuwait when in fact the allied forces outflanked the Iraqis and struck deep into Iraq via Saudi Arabia. The "cut off and kill" offensive caught the Iraqis completely off-guard and the 100-hour operation was over when the allies declared victory. The stratagem achieved what technological superiority could not.

The application of the 36 stratagems is not limited to the battlefield. In recent years, books on how these 36 stratagems can be applied in everyday life and in business have appeared in Chinese and there is also one edition in English.

Koh Kok Kiang

About the translators

Koh Kok Kiang

Koh Kok Kiang is a journalist by vocation and a quietist by inclination. His interest in cultural topics and things of the mind started in his schooling years. It was his wish to discover the wisdom of the East that has kindled his interest in Eastern philosophy. He has also translated the following titles in Asiapac Comic Series: *Book of Zen, Origins of Zen, Sayings of Lao Zi, Sayings of Lao Zi Book 2, Sayings of Lie Zi and Sayings of Zhuang Zi Book 2.*

Liu Yi

Liu Yi is currently a lecturer in English at the Shantou University in Shantou, Guangdong Province, in China. He has published articles and books on literature and translation. He has co-compiled *Selected Readings in American Literature*; published by Liaoning University Press. He has also translated *Fang Lu's Paintings*; published by Fujian People's Publishing House.

Contents

Prologue 總説 1

Stratagems When in Superior Position 勝戰計
Cross the sea under camouflage 瞞天過海 6
Besiege Wei to rescue Zhao 圍魏救趙 13
Kill with a borrowed knife 借刀殺人 20
Wait at ease for the fatigued enemy 以逸待勞 27
Loot a burning house 趁火打劫 34
Make a feint to the east while attacking
    in the west 聲東擊西 41

Stratagems for Confrontation 敵戰計
Create something out of nothing 無中生有 50
Advance to Chencang by a hidden path 暗渡陳倉 57
Watch the fire burning across the river 隔岸觀火 64
Conceal a dagger in a smile 笑裏藏刀 71
Sacrifice the plum for the peach 李代桃僵 78
Lead away a goat in passing 順手牽羊 83

Stratagems for Attack 攻戰計
Beat the grass to startle the snake 打草驚蛇 90
Raise a corpse from the dead 借屍還魂 95
Lure the tiger out of the mountain 調虎離山 102
Let the enemy off in order to snare him 欲擒姑縱 107
Cast a brick to attract a gem 拋磚引玉 112
To catch rebels, nab their leader first 擒賊擒王 119

Stratagems for Confused Situations 混戰計
Take away the fire from under the cauldron 釜底抽薪 126
Fish in troubled waters 混水摸魚 131
The cicada sheds its skin 金蟬脫殼 136

Bolt the door to catch the thief 關門捉賊 141

Befriend a distant state while attacking
  a neighbour 遠交近攻 148

Borrow a route to conquer Guo 假道伐虢 153

Stratagems for Gaining Ground 並戰計

  Replace the beams and pillars with
    rotten timber 偷梁換柱 162

  Point at the mulberry only to curse the locust 指桑罵槐 167

  Feigning foolishness 假痴不癲 172

  Remove the ladder after the ascent 上屋抽梯 179

  Putting fake blossoms on the tree 樹上開花 184

  Host and guest reversed 反客爲主 189

Stratagems for Desperate Situations 敗戰計

  Beauty trap 美人計 198

  Empty city ploy 空城計 203

  Sow discord in the enemy's camp 反間計 221

  Inflict injury on oneself to win the
    enemy's trust 苦肉計 213

  Interlocking stratagems 連環計 218

  When retreat is the best option 走爲上計 225

Prologue

Six multiplied by six equals thirty-six. Calculations produce tactics which in turn produce calculations. Each side depends upon the other. Based on this correlative relationship, ploys against the enemy are devised. Rigid application of military theory will only result in defeat on the battlefield.

總 説
zǒng shuō

六 六 三 十 六 ， 數 中 有 術 ，
liù liù sān shí liù　　shǔ zhōng yǒu shù

術 中 有 數 。 陰 陽 爕 理 ，
shù zhōng yǒu shǔ　　yīn yáng xìe lǐ

機 在 其 中 。 機 不 可 設 ，
jī zài qí zhōng　　jī bù kě shè

設 則 不 中 。
shè zé bù zhōng

Prologue

1. Assessment is objective perception of the actual situation. It is of the first order.

2. Tactics are subjective use of stratagems and are of the second order.

Assessment

Tactics

Stratagems
When in Superior Position

- **Cross the sea under camouflage**
- **Besiege Wei to rescue Zhao**
- **Kill with a borrowed knife**
- **Wait at ease for the fatigued enemy**
- **Loot a burning house**
- **Make a feint to the east while attacking in the west**

- 瞞天過海
- 圍魏救趙
- 借刀殺人
- 以逸待勞
- 趁火打劫
- 聲東擊西

Stratagem 1

Cross the sea under camouflage

The perception of perfect preparation leads to relaxed vigilance. The sight of common occurrences leads to slackened suspicion. Therefore secret machinations are better concealed in the open than in the dark, and extreme public exposure often contains extreme secrecy.

第一計
dì yī jì

瞞天過海
mán tiān guò hǎi

備 周 則 意 怠 ，　常 見 則 不 疑 。
bèi zhōu zé yì dài　　cháng jiàn zé bù yí

陰 在 陽 之 內 ，　不 在 陽 之 對 。
yīn zài yáng zhī nèi　　bù zài yáng zhī duì

太 陽 ，　太 陰 。
tài yáng　　tài yīn

Cross the sea under camouflage

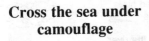

1

One who thinks that his safeguards are well-conceived is apt to relax his vigilance. Everyday occurrences will not arouse his suspicion. Thus secret plans against him can take place in the midst of common occurrences.

2 After the founder of the Sui Dynasty Yang Jian had conquered the last of the northern kingdoms during the period of the Northern and Southern Dynasties, he decided in AD 589 that the time was ripe to move south of the Yangtze River to take the Chen kingdom and consolidate his empire.

3

He Nuobi, cross the river and destroy Chen.

4 The general encamped on the northern bank of the river and set up tents and banners but did not immediately cross the river to launch an attack.

5 Disguise yourself as a businessman and buy plenty of boats.

6 He Nuobi concealed his newly-bought boats and put only a few broken vessels on the river.

7 When the dissolute king of Chen, Chen Shubao, learned that the enemy forces were just across the river, he was alarmed.

8 Our enemy has only a few broken vessels and won't be able to cross the river.

Good!

9 A few days later, there was a sudden mass movement of troops and military manoeuvres on the other side of the river.

10 Chen Shubao became agitated.

Guard the southern bank of the river!

8

9

20 Chen Shubao was still in dreamland and did not have any defence ready.

At dawn, He Nuobi's troops reached the other side of the river and mounted a surprise attack on the unprepared Chen forces.

21

The Sui troops easily took the Chen capital in today's Nanjing and destroyed the Chen kingdom. The fragmentation of China under the Northern and Southern Dynasties thus came to an end.

I surrender!

22

23 This stratagem uses false appearances to lull the enemy into complacency while massing troops for attack. When an invasion is launched, the enemy will be caught napping.

Stratagem 2

Besiege Wei to save Zhao

It is wiser to launch an attack against the enemy forces when they are dispersed than to fight them when they are concentrated. He who strikes first fails and he who strikes late prevails.

第二計
dì èr jì

圍魏救趙
wéi wèi jiù zhào

共 敵 不 如 分 敵 ，
gòng dí bù rú fēn dí

敵 陽 不 如 敵 陰 。
dí yáng bù rú dí yīn

Besiege Wei
to save Zhao

1. It is more difficult to attack the united enemy forces than the scattered ones.

2. Patience and not haste in attack is more likely to lead to victory.

3. This stratagem originates from the Warring States period. In 354 BC, the king of Wei sent general Pang Juan to attack Handan, the capital of Zhao.

4 Wei laid siege to Zhao for a year. Both Zhao's and Wei's troops became weakened and exhausted.

5 The king of Qi was approached by Zhao for help and he decided to send his troops to save Zhao.

I appoint Tian Ji as commander and Sun Bin as military adviser.

6 Tian Ji said:

Let's all go directly to Handan to relieve Zhao.

7 But Sun Bin suggested:

Trying to help Zhao during a siege is like trying to unravel a tangled knot, and sending troops to Handan is like using a fist to unravel the knot. We're unlikely to succeed.

12 Tian Ji took Sun Bin's advice and made a diversionary attack on Wei's capital Daliang coupled with an ambush along the mountain pass at Guiling which Pang Juan's troops had to go through on their return journey to Wei.

13 General Pang, Daliang is under attack!

14 Return to save Daliang!

15 The worried Wei troops made haste to return to their capital and in the process wore themselves out.

Quick!

19

The Qi troops won because of two reasons.

20 One, they intervened when both the Zhao and the Wei troops were weakened after their long confrontation.

21 Two, when they attacked the weakly-defended Wei, the Wei troops in Zhao became worried and confused.

When attacking, eliminate your enemy's would-be saviour and the retreating enemy. In this way you can beat a strong enemy.

Stratagem 3

Kill with a borrowed knife

Your enemy's situation is clear but your ally's stand
is uncertain. At this time, induce your ally to attack
your enemy in order to preserve your strength. In
dialectic terms, another man's loss is your gain.

第三計

dì sān jì

借刀殺人

jiè dāo shā rén

敵 巳 明 ， 友 未 定 ， 引 友 殺 敵

dí yǐ míng　　yǒu wèi dìng　　yǐng yǒu shā dí

不 自 出 力 ， 以 《 損 》 推 演 。

bù zì chū lì　　yǐ　　sǔn　　tuī yǎn

Kill with a borrowed knife

1

If it is obvious that your enemy will fight but your ally is uncertain, induce the ally to attack your enemy so as to preserve your strength.

2

First I must get rid of Kuai's loyal officials and able generals.

During the Spring and Autumn period, the duke of Zheng wanted to attack Kuai state.

3

Find out who are the capable officials and generals in Kuai.

Yes.

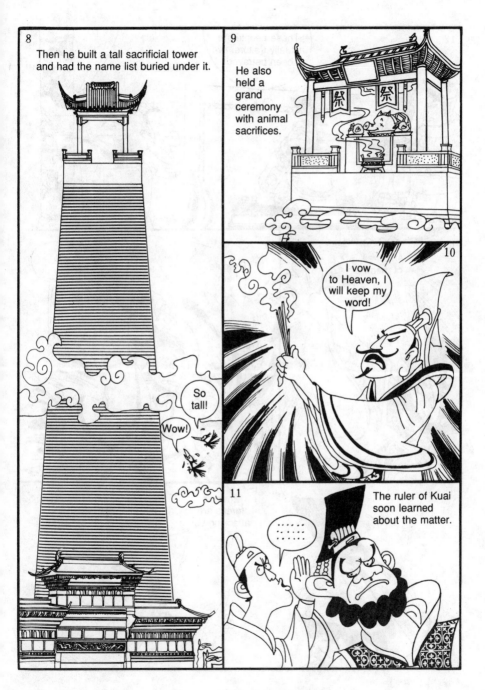

24

16

Who's going to lead our defence? Who has sound strategies?

17 The duke of Zheng led his troops to Kuai and easily conquered the state.

18

Borrow Borrow Borrow

"Borrow" can mean making use of the enemy to cause its self-destruction.

19 Use ruses to sow discord among the enemy and make them kill one another. This is making use of the enemy's own knife.

20   To get hold of the enemy and use them is borrowing the enemy's resources.

21   To sow discord among the enemy's generals, making them fight among themselves, is to borrow the enemy's generals.

22   To find out the enemy's strategy and turn it to one's advantage is to borrow the enemy's strategy.

This can be a political as well as a military stratagem. One can make use of a third party to deal with another or make use of the enemy to destroy itself.

Stratagem 4

Wait at ease for the fatigued enemy

To weaken the enemy, it is not necessary to attack
him directly. Tire him by carrying out an active
defence, and in doing so, his strength will be
reduced, and your side will gain the upper hand.
This is weakening the strong to benefit the weak.

第四計

dì sì jì

以逸待勞

yǐ yì dài láo

困 敵 之 勢 ， 不 以 戰 ；

kùn dí zhī shì bù yǐ zhàn

損 剛 益 柔 。

sǔn gāng yì róu

Wait at ease for the fatigued enemy

1 To counter a powerful enemy, it's not necessary to confront them directly and immediately.

Let's fight!

2 You're too weak!

3 Hard and soft, strong and weak can be interchangeable states.

You're conceited too soon!

4 Putting up a strong defence can gradually deplete the strength of the enemy. When the strong enemy becomes weak, one can gain the upper hand.

You're right!

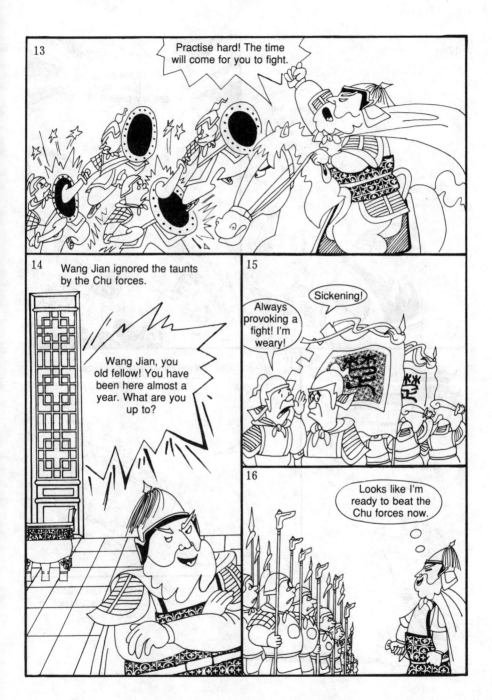

Stratagem 5

Loot a burning house

When the enemy falls into a severe crisis, exploit
his adversity and attack by direct confrontation.
This is the strong defeating the weak.

第五計
dì wǔ jì

趁火打劫
chèn huǒ dǎ jié

敵 之 害 大 ， 就 勢 取 利 ，
dí zhī hài dà   jiù shì qǔ lì

剛 決 柔 也 。
gāng jué róu yě

Loot a burning house

9 Gou Jian bribed Wu's minister Bo Pi with eight beautiful women and a thousand ounces of gold.

10 Wu's counsellor Wu Zixu had false charges pressed against him and he committed suicide.

11 Wu was hit by a severe drought.

I'm dying!

Rain! Water! Water!

12 Meanwhile, Wu's king Fu Chai wasted his resources on buildings for his pleasure.

I want a magnificent palace!

38

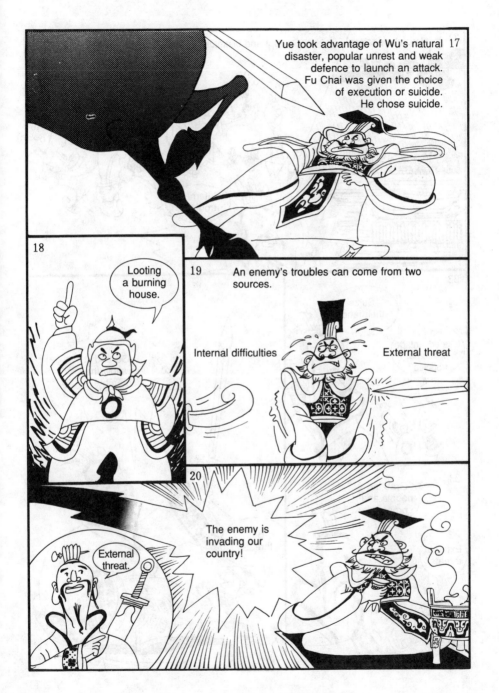

17 Yue took advantage of Wu's natural disaster, popular unrest and weak defence to launch an attack. Fu Chai was given the choice of execution or suicide. He chose suicide.

18 Looting a burning house.

19 An enemy's troubles can come from two sources.

Internal difficulties

External threat

20 The enemy is invading our country!

External threat.

39

Make a feint to the east while attacking in the west

When the enemy command is in confusion, it will be unprepared for any contingencies. The situation is like flood waters rising higher and higher; likely to burst the dam at any time. When the enemy loses internal control, take the chance and destroy him.

第六計

dì liù jì

聲東擊西

shēng dōng jì xī

敵 志 亂 萃 ， 不 虞 ，
dí zhì luàn cuì bù yú

坤 下 兌 上 之 象 ，
kūn xià duì shàng zhī xiàng

利 其 不 自 主 而 取 之 。
lì qí bù zì zhǔ ér qǔ zhī

Make a feint to the east while attacking in the west

5

In AD 200, Yuan Shao and Cao Cao fought a decisive battle. Yuan Shao, with the advantage of terrain and troop strength, wanted to block the enemy's route of retreat.

Battle of Guandu.

7

General Yan Liang, lead 10,000 soldiers to occupy the enemy's strategic Baima city so that we can quickly wipe them out.

Yes!

8

Cao Cao was told of the enemy's plan.

Baima is in imminent danger and the defending general seeks help.

9

Cao Cao summoned his aides to help think of a solution.

What to do?

We're short of men here.

Send reinforcements.

43

45

46

47

Stratagems for Confrontation

- **Create something out of nothing**
- **Advance to Chencang by a hidden path**
- **Watch the fire burning across the river**
- **Conceal a dagger in a smile**
- **Sacrifice the plum for the peach**
- **Lead away a goat in passing**

- 無中生有
- 暗渡陳倉
- 隔岸觀火
- 笑裏藏刀
- 李代桃僵
- 順手牽羊

Stratagem 7

Create something out of nothing

Design a counterfeit front to put the enemy
off-guard. When the trick works, the front is
changed into something real so that the enemy will
be thrown into a state of double confusion. In short,
deceptive appearances often conceal some
forthcoming dangers.

第七計
dì qī jì

無中生有
wú zhōng shēng yǒu

誑 也 ， 非 誑 也 ，
kuáng yě   fēi kuáng yě

實 其 所 誑 也 。
shí qí shuǒ kuáng yě

少 陰 ， 太 陰 ， 太 陽 。
shǎo yīn   tài yīn   tài yáng

Create something out of nothing

53

54

28 He's simple-minded and easily taken in.

29 He's over-cautious and hesitant in deploying troops.

30 Such people are susceptible to this ruse.

Secondly, the timing. When the enemy is blind to your intentions, change from false to real and mount a surprise attack.

31

From false to real, from nothing to something. The false can only delude the enemy. It takes the real to overcome the enemy.

From false to real is deception. Do it too often and you'll be exposed.

32

56

Stratagem 8

Advance to Chencang by a hidden path

To pin down the enemy, expose part of your action deliberately, so that you can make a surprise attack somewhere else.

第八計
dì bā jì

暗渡陳倉
àn dù chén cāng

示 之 以 動 ， 利 其 静 而 有 主 ，
shì zhī yǐ dòng   lì qí jìng ér yǒu zhǔ

「 益 動 而 巽 。 」
yì dòng ér xùn

Advance to Chencang
by a hidden path

1 Deliberately expose part of your action to lead the enemy into your trap.

2 Then make an attack from somewhere else.

3 It took place towards the end of the Qin dynasty.

This is called "repair the plank road openly while advancing to Chencang by a hidden path".

4 There were rebellions everywhere and the most powerful of the rebel leaders was Xiang Yu.

I'm the warlord of Western Chu.

58

59

10 Once Liu Bang arrived in Hanzhong, he made Han Xin commander of his army. After nine years of preparations, Liu Bang's army became powerful and was ready to march eastwards.

11

12
We need not enter Guanzhong directly to unite the territories. Scheme to attack from the east.

Han Xin, what is your strategy for conquest?

13
The plank road is already destroyed. How are we to enter Guanzhong?

14
There're two ways of entering Guanzhong - by the plank road and the old route through Chencang.

* 1 li is about one kilometre.

Stratagem 9

Watch the fire burning across the river

When a serious conflict breaks out within the enemy alliance, wait quietly for the chaos to build up. Because once its internal conflict intensifies, the alliance will bring destruction upon itself. As for you, observe closely and make preparations for any advantage that may come from it.

第九計
dì jiǔ jì

隔岸觀火
gé àn guān huǒ

| 陽 | 乖 | 序 | 亂 | ， | 陰 | 以 | 作 | 逆 | 。 |
| yáng | guāi | xù | luàn | | yīn | yǐ | dài | nì | |

| 暴 | 戾 | 恣 | 睢 | ， | 其 | 勢 | 自 | 斃 | 。 |
| bào | lì | zì | suī | | qí | shì | zì | bì | |

| 順 | 以 | 動 | 豫 | ， | 豫 | 順 | 以 | 動 | 。 |
| shùn | yǐ | dòng | yù | | yù | shùn | yǐ | dòng | |

Watch the fire burning across the river

65

Towards the end of the Eastern Han dynasty, Cao Cao defeated Yuan Shao's forces in the Battle of Guandu.

66

After Yuan Shao's death, his three sons fought among themselves in a battle of succession.

8

Cao Cao's forces are attacking again!

9

11

Cao Cao's strategist, Guo Jia suggested:

The Yuan brothers were fighting among themselves and our attack only caused them to unite against us.

Unite against our common enemy!

10

68

70

Stratagem 10

Conceal a dagger in a smile

One way or another, make the enemy trust you and
thereby slacken his vigilance. Meanwhile, plot
secretly, making preparations for your future action
to ensure its success. In this stratagem, one conceals
one's hostility by assuming outward friendliness.

第十計

dì shí jì

笑裏藏刀

xiào lǐ cáng dāo

信 而 安 之 ，　陰 以 圖 之 ；
xìn ér ān zhī　　yīn yǐ tú zhī

備 而 後 動 ，　勿 使 有 變 。
bèi ér hòu dòng　cōng shǐ yǒu biàn

剛 中 柔 外 也 。
gāng zhōng róu wài yě

Conceal a dagger in a smile

72

73

21 The Qin soldiers then disguised themselves as Wei's troops and went to the city gates.

Open the gates! Gongzi Ying is back!

22 The Qin troops charged through the gates and conquered Wu city.

I'm being taken captive to Qin.

23 Learn from him. Don't be taken in by the enemy's nice-sounding words!

24 This stratagem is used to describe those who hide evil intentions behind a benign front. I use it as a military tactic.

Gongsun Yang achieved his victory by taking advantage of personal ties to hide his military objectives. Gongzi Ying trusted him too readily and this led to his as well as Wei's downfall.

Stratagem 11

Sacrifice the plum for the peach

When loss is inevitable, sacrifice the part for the benefit of the whole.

第十一計

dì shí yī jì

李代桃僵

lǐ dài táo jiāng

勢 必 有 損 ， 損 陰 以 益 陽 。

shì bì yǒu sǔn   sǔn yīn yǐ yì yáng

Sacrifice the plum for the peach

1 When the worm comes to gnaw the peach tree, the plum tree offers itself as a sacrifice.

I'm yours!

2 In military strategy, if loss is to be incurred, it is better to lose something for the sake of victory.

3 In the Warring States period, Qi commander Tian Ji always lost in his horse races with one of the princes.

Lost again.

4 Sun Bin said:

There is not much difference between the horses. I've a plan to ensure that you'll win.

Really?

5 Pit your least strong horse against his strongest.

Your strongest against his less strong.

And your less strong against his least strong.

6

7 Although I lost one race I won two.

8 In the year 353 BC, Sun Bin's use of the "besiege Wei to save Zhao" strategy sent the Wei troops rushing back to defend their state.

9 The Wei troops split into three columns of left, centre and right in their return journey.

Stratagem 12

Lead away a goat in passing

Exploit any minor lapses on the enemy side, and
seize every advantage to your side. Any
negligence of the enemy must be turned into a
benefit for you.

第十二計

dì shí èr jì

順手牽羊

shùn shǒu qiān yáng

微 隙 在 所 必 乘 ；

wēi xì zài shuǒ bì chéng

微 利 在 所 必 得 。

wēi xì zài shuǒ bì dé

少 陰 ， 少 陽 。

shǎo yīn shǎo yáng

Lead away a goat in passing

1

In a war, be quick to exploit any weakness of the enemy. Any oversight of theirs must be looked upon as an opportunity for us.

2

Just before a large army enters battle, its shortcomings will be exposed. Exploiting them will lead to victory.

3

The duke of Song has no respect for the king of Zhou!

In the year 770 BC, the duke of Zheng joined forces with Lu and Qi to attack Song.

87

Stratagems for Attack

- **Beat the grass to startle the snake**
- **Raise a corpse from the dead**
- **Lure the tiger out of the mountain**
- **Let the enemy off in order to snare him**
- **Cast a brick to attract a gem**
- **To catch rebels, nab their leader first**

- 打草驚蛇
- 借屍還魂
- 調虎離山
- 欲擒故縱
- 拋磚引玉
- 擒賊擒王

Stratagem 13

Beat the grass to startle the snake

Any suspicion about the enemy's circumstances must be investigated. Before any military action, be sure to ascertain the enemy's situation; repeated reconnaissance is an effective way to discover the hidden enemy.

第十三計

dì shí sān jì

打草驚蛇

dǎ cǎo jīng sé

疑 以 叩 實 ， 察 而 後 動 ；

yí yǐ kòu shí chá ér hòu dòng

復 者 ， 陰 之 媒 也 。

fù zhě yīn zhī méi yě

Beat the grass to startle the snake

9　The Qin troops arrived at Mount Xiao.

Advance!

10　His two assistant generals Xi Qi and Bai Yi warned him:

We are attacking Zheng after Hua. The overlord state of Jin won't like this. Now that we are at Mount Xiao, we should be careful.

Mount Xiao is a dangerous place. We should search out its paths to make sure it's safe.

12

11　Meng Mingshi did not think it was necessary to take precautions.

We're strong. There's nothing to fear.

Let's charge and finish them off!

Jin's troops!

93

94

Stratagem 14

Raise a corpse from the dead

The powerful is beyond exploitation, but the weak
needs help. Exploit and manipulate the weak for
they need you more than you need them.

第十四計

dì shí sì jì

借屍還魂

jiè   shī   huán   hún

有 用 者 ， 不 可 借 ；

yǒu yòng zhě   bù kě jiè

不 能 用 者 ， 求 借 。

bù néng yòng zhě   qiú jiè

借 不 能 用 者 而 用 之 ，

jiè bù néng yòng zhě ér yòng zhī

匪 我 求 童 蒙 ， 童 蒙 求 我 。

fěi wǒ qiú tóng méng   tóng méng qiú wǒ

Raise a corpse
from the dead

9 Liu Bei thought:

Jingzhou is barren after years of warfare. Where can I go to expand my base?

10 To expand his base, Cao Cao launched an attack on Hanzhong which was defended by Zhang Lu.

11 Yizhou administrator Liu Zhang whose state bordered Hanzhong became very worried.

12 His adviser Zhang Song suggested:

Once Cao Cao has conquered Hanzhong, he'll come for Yizhou. Why not enlist Liu Bei's help in subduing Hanzhong and together with him resist Cao Cao?

13. Liu Bei and I are both scions of the Han Dynasty and Cao Cao's enemy. It's best to seek his help.

14. Liu Zhang despatched Fa Zheng to seek Liu Bei's help. Liu Bei was pleased.

15. Liu Zhang is weak, incompetent and unpopular with many officials. I hope you'll take this chance to seize Yizhou. Zhang Song and I will help you in secret.

All right.

16. Under the pretext of fighting Zhang Lu, Liu Bei entered Yizhou's territory and obtained much supplies and reinforcements.

17 Liu Bei also took the opportunity to improve the people's lot and win their support.

Liu Bei is good.

Back him.

18 Liu Bei's military adviser Pang Tong told him:

Pretend to return to Jingzhou. Find a pretext to seize Baisui Pass and use it as a base to attack Yizhou.

19 After two years of warfare, Liu Bei conquered the territory in today's Sichuan.

20 With all these territories, I can build up my power base.

Stratagem 15

Lure the tiger out of the mountain

Use unfavourable natural conditions to trap the
enemy in a difficult position. Use deception to lure
him out. In an offensive that involves great risk lure
the enemy to come out against you.

第 十 五 計
dì shí wǔ jì

調虎離山
diào hǔ lí shān

待 天 以 困 之 ，　用 人 以 誘 之 ，
dài tiān yǐ kùn zhī 　 yòng rén yǐ yòu zhī

往 蹇 來 返 。
wǎng jiǎn lái fǎn

Lure the tiger
out of the mountain

104

13 Liu Xun possessed fertile land and a strong army, and he was also keen to boost his power and control of neighbouring territories.

I'll lead the army to attack Shangliao.

14 He ignored the warnings by his own officials.

Shangliao is well-fortified. Sun Ce's army might invade us while you're away.

15 As a result, Sun Ce easily seized control of Lujiang.

16 Liu Xun failed to take Shangliao and lost his base as well. He led his army to join Cao Cao.

This is how the stratagem works.

This stratagem involves using deception to make the enemy deploy his forces to your advantage and to achieve your objective.

Stratagem 16

Let the enemy off in order to snare him

Press the enemy forces too hard and they will strike back fiercely. Let them go and their morale will sink. Follow them closely, but do not push them too hard. Tire them out and sap their morale; capture them when they are in panic and flee helter-skelter. In this way, victory is won without shedding blood. In short, careful delay in attack will help to bring destruction to the enemy.

第十六計

dì shí liù jì

欲擒故縱

yù qín gù zòng

逼	則	反	兵 ；	走	則	減	勢 。
bī	zé	fǎn	bīng	zhǒu	zé	jiǎn	shì

緊	隨	勿	迫 ，	纍	其	氣	力 ，
jǐn	suí	cōng	pò	lèi	qí	qì	lì

消	其	鬥	志 ，	散	而	後	擒 ，
xiāo	qí	dòu	zhì	sàn	ér	hòu	qín

兵	不	血	刃 。	需 ，	有	孚 ，	光 。
bīng	bù	xuè	rèn	xū	yǒu	fú	guāng

Let the enemy off in order to snare him

1
If you close in on the enemy leaving it no way out, it will strike back out of desperation.

2
If you leave them an escape route, their tempers will subside.

3
Follow the enemy closely but don't press them too hard. Fritter away their strength and sap their morale.

4 When the enemy is no longer able to function as a united force, you can subdue them without shedding blood.

5 In the year 506 BC, Wu joined forces with two other states and overwhelmed the army of Chu.

6 The king of Wu, He Lu led troops in pursuit until they reached Qingfa.

Let's crush them.

7 His younger brother Fu Gai stopped him.

A cornered beast will fight to the finish, what more armed troops?

8 If the Chu troops have no choice but to fight for their survival, they'll put up a spirited defence and it'll be difficult to vanquish them.

9 The king took his brother's advice.

Give them a chance to flee across the river.

10 Cross the river and we will be safe.

11 The Chu soldiers were so busy running for their lives that they lost the morale to fight.

Let's cross the river.

Stratagem 17

Cast a brick to attract a gem

Use bait to lure the enemy and take him in.

第十七計

dì shí qī jì

抛磚引玉

pāo zhuān yǐng yù

類 以 誘 之 ， 擊 蒙 也 。

lèi yǐ yòu zhī   jī méng yě

Cast a brick to attract a gem

114

115

12 On the third day...

Light 30,000 stoves.

13 After pursuing the retreating Qi troops for three days, Pang Juan counted the number of Qi campsite stove fires. He was overjoyed.

I knew the Qi troops feared combat. Now more than half of them have deserted.

14 Confident of victory, Pang Juan left his foot soldiers behind and led cavalry troops to give chase.

15 Sun Bin had been tracking the progress of the Wei pursuers.

They'll reach Malin tonight.

20 The Wei troops indeed arrived after dark.

What's this?

21 Light torches!

22 The Wei troops were doomed and Pang Juan took his own life.

There're many ways to deal with the enemy, but to catch him unawares is the best.

Stratagem 18

To catch rebels, nab their leader first

Destroy the enemy crack forces and capture their chief, and the enemy will collapse. His situation will be as desperate as a sea dragon fighting on land.

第十八計

dì shí bā jì

擒賊擒王

qín zéi qín wáng

摧 其 堅 ， 奪 有 魁 ，

cuī qí jiān duó yǒu kuí

以 解 其 體 。

yǐ jiě qí tǐ

龍 戰 於 野 ， 其 道 窮 也 。

lóng zhàn yú yě qí dào qióng yě

To catch rebels, nab their leader first

1 Wipe out the enemy's main force and capture its chief. In this way, the enemy's power will be sapped.

2 Once the dragon leaves the sea, it can't exert its power.

I can't influence winds and waves.

3 There're many ways to achieve victory on the battlefield.

7 In the year AD 756, rebel commander Yin Ziqi led 100,000 soldiers to besiege the strategic city of Suiyang.

8 Zhang Xun was in charge of its defence and repelled the enemy attacks many times.

9 Their forces must be exhausted. If we attack them tonight and nab Yin Ziqi first they'll be in disarray.

10 That night, the defenders charged out of Suiyang.

11 Zhang Xun is attacking us!

The enemies were still asleep.

12 Zhang Xun fought his way to the main rebel camp.

We've killed many of their officers and men. But we can't find Yin Ziqi.

Stratagems
for Confused Situations

- **Take away the fire from under the cauldron**
- **Fish in troubled waters**
- **The cicada sheds its skin**
- **Bolt the door to catch the thief**
- **Befriend a distant state while attacking a neighbour**
- **Borrow a route to conquer Guo**

- 釜底抽薪
- 混水摸魚
- 金蟬脫殼
- 關門捉賊
- 遠交近攻
- 假道伐虢

Stratagem 19

Take away the fire from under the cauldron

When confronted with a powerful enemy, do not fight them head-on but try to find their weakest spot to initiate their collapse. This is the weak overcoming the strong.

第十九計

dì shí jiǔ jì

釜底抽薪

fǔ dǐ chōu xīn

不 敵 其 力 ， 而 消 其 勢 ，

bù dí qí lì   ér xiāo qí shì

兑 不 乾 上 之 象 。

duì bù gān shàng zhī xiàng

Take away the fire from under the cauldron

4

Don't fight a powerful enemy head-on, instead undermine its morale and deprive it of leadership.

5

During the reign of Han emperor Jing Di in the year 154 BC, the prince of Wu, Liu Bi, and the prince of Chu, Liu Wu, joined forces with seven other states to stage a rebellion. They first attacked the state of Liang.

6

Han marshal Zhou Yafu felt that the Wu and Chu forces were formidable and could not be easily beaten in a clash. But if their supplies were cut off, they could be defeated and the siege of Liang would be lifted.

7

Having decided on a strategy, Zhou Yafu headed for Yingyang.

8 Let's rush to Yingyang before the enemy's supplies arrive!

9 Zhou Yafu made a detour around the enemy and arrived at Yingyang.

Guard Yingyang.

10 Zhou Yafu himself withdrew to set up camp at Maoyi to seize the enemy's provisions and to seal off their supply route.

11 Fix crossbows around Daying. When the enemy attacks, just defend and hold your ground. Do not attack.

Stratagem 20

Fish in troubled waters

When the enemy falls into internal chaos, exploit his
weakened position and lack of direction and win
him over to your side. This is as natural as people
going to bed at the end of the day.

第二十計

dì èr shí jì

混水摸魚

hùn shuǐ mō yú

乘 其 陰 亂 ， 利 其 弱 而 無 主 。

chéng qí yīn luàn lì qí luò ér wú zhǔ

隨 ， 以 向 晦 入 宴 息 。

suí yǐ xiàng huì rù yàn xī

4 During the late Eastern Han Dynasty, Yuan Shao and Cao Cao squared off in the famous Battle of Guandu. Yuan Shao had 100,000 soldiers and ample provisions.

With 20,000 soldiers and inadequate supplies, how can Cao Cao be my match?

5 Cao Cao's adviser Xu You, a defector from Yuan Shao's camp, suggested a plan.

Great!

6 Disguise 5,000 soldiers as Yuan Shao's troops.

7 It's pitch dark tonight. Head for Yuan Shao's supply base at Wucao.

133

8

Where are you from?

Yuan Shao's back-up troops.

On the way they met some of Yuan Shao's troops.

9

Here's Yuan Shao's supply base.

After bluffing his way through, Cao Cao arrived at Wucao.

10

Cao Cao's troops set the base on fire, sparking panic among the enemy forces.

Who started the fire?

11

Destroy all supplies and wipe out the base!

12

"An army cannot fight on an empty stomach", and with supplies gone, Yuan Shao's troops lost their nerve and were easily defeated. Cao Cao's forces annihilated 80,000 enemy soldiers.

13

To secure victory, first create disorder in the enemy camp and quickly take advantage of the ensuing chaos to achieve your objective.

14

Even muddied water will soon become clear, so act quickly or the enemy will see through the plan.

This stratagem must be used with caution. It can be employed but not relied upon as there're other factors to be considered.

135

Stratagem 21

The cicada sheds its skin

Make your front array appear as if you are
still holding your position so that the allied
forces will not suspect your intention and
the enemy troops will not dare to attack rashly.
Then withdraw your main forces secretly.

第二十一計

dì èr shí yī jì

金蟬脫殼

jīn chán tuō kè

存 其 形 ， 完 其 勢 ； 友 不 疑 ，

cún qí xíng　　wán qí shì　　yǒu bù yí

敵 不 動 。 巽 而 止 蠱 。

dí bù dòng　　xùn ér zhǐ gǔ

The cicada sheds its skin

1

Maintain one's original position and keep up appearances.

2

This place is heavily defended and not easy to attack.

Right!

3

When the enemy is not suspicious of you, secretly move your forces.

Moving about in secret!

4 During the reign of Emperor Ning Zong of the Southern Song Dynasty, the Jin tribal army attacked China. A capable general, Bi Daibi, beat off the Jin attack.

5 But the determined Jin sent tens of thousands of cavalry soldiers to besiege the Song camp.

7 Don't panic. I've an excellent plan for retreat.

6 The Song forces were very worried.

We've only a few thousand soldiers. How to resist them?

139

140

Stratagem 22

Bolt the door to catch the thief

When dealing with a small and weak enemy,
surround and destroy him. If you let him
retreat, you will be at a disadvantage
in pursuing him.

第二十二計

dì èr shí èr jì

關門捉賊

guān mén zhuō zéi

小 敵 困 之 ， 剝 ，

xiǎo dí kùn zhī bō

不 利 有 攸 往 。

bù lì yǒu yōu wǎng

Bolt the door to catch the thief

1 If the enemy is weak, surround them and finish them off.

2 If the enemy is small in number, it is not wise to pursue for they're nimble in movement.

3 Surround them and cut off all routes of escape. Then they will be at your mercy.

142

4 If the "thief" is allowed to escape, it may make a comeback.

5 I understand. Although the enemy is weak, one must finish them for good.

6 This strategy of elimination is not restricted to the smaller enemy. Depending on the battle situation, a stronger enemy can also be wiped out in this way.

7 In the year 260 BC, the armies of Qin and Zhao met in a decisive battle.

8 Qin used the strategy of sowing discord among the enemy to cause the Zhao commander Lian Po, an experienced general, to be replaced by an armchair strategist, Zhao Kuo.

Now I'm in charge.

9 Qin general Bai Qi ordered:

Take our main forces to Changbi in Qin and be well-entrenched there. Block off all exits.

10 Take 3,000 soldiers to lure the Zhao troops out.

11 Zhao Kuo did not know about the trap and when the Qin deliberately let him win his first battle, he was extremely elated and cocky.

145

146

Stratagem 23

Befriend a distant state while attacking a neighbour

It is more advantageous to conquer the nearby
enemies, because of geographical reasons, than
those far away. So ally yourself temporarily
with your distant enemies
in spite of political differences.

第二十三計
dì èr shí sān jì

遠交近攻
yuǎn jiāo jìn gōng

形 禁 勢 格 ，　　利 從 近 取 ，
xíng jìn shì gé　　　lì cóng jìn qǔ

害 以 遠 隔 。　　上 火 下 澤 。
hài yǐ yuǎn gé　　　shàng huǒ xià zé

Befriend a distant state while attacking a neighbour

1 If military objectives are limited by geographical factors, it's better to conquer nearby rather than distant states.

2 To attack a distant state is hazardous.

3 Even if one has political differences with a distant enemy, one must maintain harmonious ties temporarily so as to achieve one's military objectives.

4 During the Warring States period, Zhao Xiang was the king of Qin. His prime minister Duke Rang wanted to boost his stature and suggested to the king:

We should attack the distant state of Qi to expand our influence.

5 When Fan Sui heard about this, he quickly remonstrated with the king.

6 For a large and powerful state like ours to conquer the territories of dukes and princes is as easy a task as using the famed black hounds of Han to catch rabbits.

7 But Qin has been inward-looking and without major accomplishments for 15 years. This is partly due to the incompetence of Duke Rang and Your Majesty's oversight.

151

12 The king was pleased and in the year 266 BC, Fan Sui was made the prime minister. Qin acted according to his plan and made peace with the distant Qi and Chu while attacking Han.

Within 10 years Qin swallowed Han, followed by Zhao, Wei, Chu, Yan and finally Qi. China was unified for the first time in its history under the Qin Dynasty.

13

14 The flame flickers upwards and water flows downwards. In nature, opposites can serve the same end of nourishing life. In strategy, totally different approaches can be used to achieve one and the same purpose.

In this strategy, befriending a distant state is not forever, but only to buy time while dealing with nearby targets. Once the nearby ones are conquered, the distant state will be the next target.

Stratagem 24

Borrow a route to conquer Guo

When a small state, located between two big states,
is being threatened by the enemy state, you
should immediately send troops to rescue it, thereby
expanding your sphere of influence. Mere talk
cannot win the trust of a state which is
in a difficult position.

第二十四計

dì èr shí sì jì

假道伐虢

jiǎ dào fá guó

兩 大 之 間 ， 敵 脅 以 從 ，

liǎng dà zhī jiān　　dí xié yǐ cóng

我 假 以 勢 。

wǒ jiǎ yǐ shì

困 ， 有 言 不 信 。

kùn　　yǒu yǎn bù xìn

Borrow a route to conquer Guo

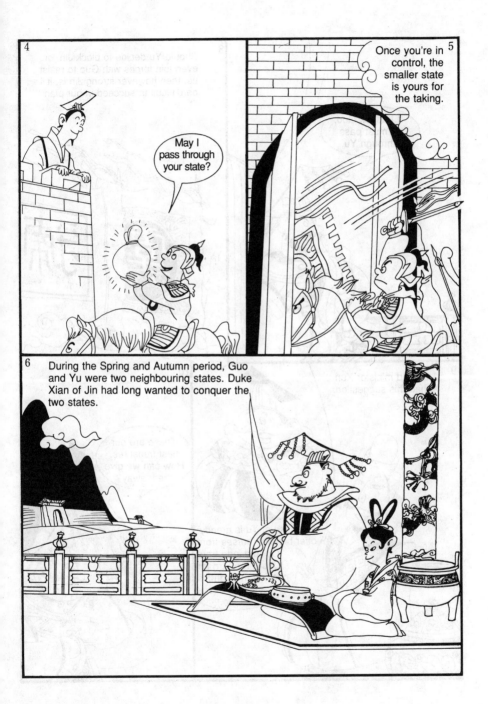

155

Panel 7:
If I attack Guo, I must pass through Yu.

Panel 8:
Should Yu decide to block Jin, or even join forces with Guo to resist us, then however strong Jin is, it'll be difficult to succeed in our plan.

Panel 9:
A trusted minister Xun Xi had this suggestion:

The duke of Yu is greedy; offer him fine horses from Qu and jade from Chuiji in return for passing through his state to attack Guo.

Panel 10:
These are our best treasures. How can we give them away?

11

We're merely temporarily transferring them from our storehouse to Yu's. Eventually they'll be reclaimed by us.

12 Duke Xian despatched Xun Xi to Yu to obtain safe passage.

Guo has made incursions across our border. We'd like to pass through your state to Guo to demand an explanation.

13

Permission granted. I'll also personally lead a punitive expedition to Guo.

14 But the shrewd Yu minister Gong Zhiqi strongly opposed the move:

Yu and Guo depend on each other for security. If Guo is destroyed, it will be the case of "if the lips are gone, the teeth will be cold".

My mind is set. Speak no more.

15 Gong Zhiqi couldn't bear to see his home and state destroyed, so he hastily summoned all his clansmen and they fled to Cao state.

16 Jin despatched general Li Ke and Xun Xi to invade Guo. After almost four months, Guo was destroyed.

Stratagems
for Gaining Ground

- **Replace the beams and pillars with rotten timber**
- **Point at the mulberry only to curse the locust**
- **Feigning foolishness**
- **Remove the ladder after the ascent**
- **Putting fake blossoms on the tree**
- **Host and guest reversed**

- 偷樑換柱
- 指桑罵槐
- 假痴不癲
- 上屋抽梯
- 樹上開花
- 反客為主

Replace the beams and pillars
with rotten timber

Make the allied forces change their battle formation
frequently so that their main strength will be taken
away. When they collapse by themselves, go and
swallow them up. This is like pulling back the
wheels of a chariot to control its direction.

第二十五計
dì èr shí wǔ jì

偷樑換柱
tōu liáng huàn zhù

頻 更 其 陣 ，　抽 其 勁 旅 ，
pín gèng qí zhèn　chōu qí jìng lǚ

待 其 自 敗 ，　而 後 乘 之 。
dài qí zì bài　ér hòu chéng zhī

曳 其 輪 也 。
yè qí lún yě

Replace the beams and pillars with rotten timber

1 A typical battle formation has a central axle (heavenly beam) extending from the front to the rear and a horizontal axle (earthly pillar) connecting the right and left flanks. The two axles are made up of the best fighters.

2 When joining forces with allies to fight a common enemy, secretly infiltrate the allies' battle formations so that you can control or subjugate the allies.

3 That's treachery!

4 Another way is to secretly get hold of your enemy's "beams and pillars".

5 That's brilliant.

6 Before the Warring States period, in the state of Jin, the four noble families of Zhi, Zhao, Han and Wei shared power.

7 The Zhi clan was the most powerful.

You should all cede more territory to me.

8 But Zhao bitterly opposed the idea.

No way!

9 In the year 451 BC...

Han and Wei, join me to attack the Zhao clan!

15 Zhang Mengtan managed to secure the backing of Han and Wei.

16 After eliminating Zhao, Zhi intends to attack Han and Wei. Why don't we join forces to destroy Zhi?

Good!

At night, the Han and Wei soldiers secretly dug up the dikes, causing the water to flood Zhi's camp.

17

18 Water flooded Zhi's camp and utterly destroyed Zhi's soldiers.

Where did the torrent come from?

19 The Zhi chief was captured.

Kill all the Zhi clansmen. Divide their territory.

20 Stop the wheel and you can control the carriage's movement. However beautiful a building is, remove the beams and pillars and it will collapse.

When confronting a powerful enemy, adopt feints, sudden manoeuvres, and split the enemy strength to weaken it. Victory is then secured.

Stratagem 26

Point at the mulberry only to curse the locust

When the powerful wants to rule over the weak, he
will sound a warning. One's uncompromising
stand will often win loyalty, and one's
resolute action, respect.

第二十六計

dì èr shí liù jì

指桑罵槐

zhǐ sāng mà huái

大 凌 小 者 ，　警 以 誘 之 。

dà líng xiǎo zhě　jǐng yǐ yòu zhī

剛 中 而 應 ，　行 險 而 順 。

gāng zhōng ér yìng　xíng xiǎn ér shùn

Point at the mulberry only to curse the locust

5 Chen, Cai, Zhu and Song attended the meeting.

Lu, Wei, Zheng, Cao are not here.

⁉

6 I want the support of the other states to deal with Lu first.

7 The duke of Song said:

Count me out. I'm going home.

Guan Zhong said:

Song is far and Lu is near. Let's deal with Lu first.

8 Duke Huan was furious.

9 Launch an attack on Song.

170

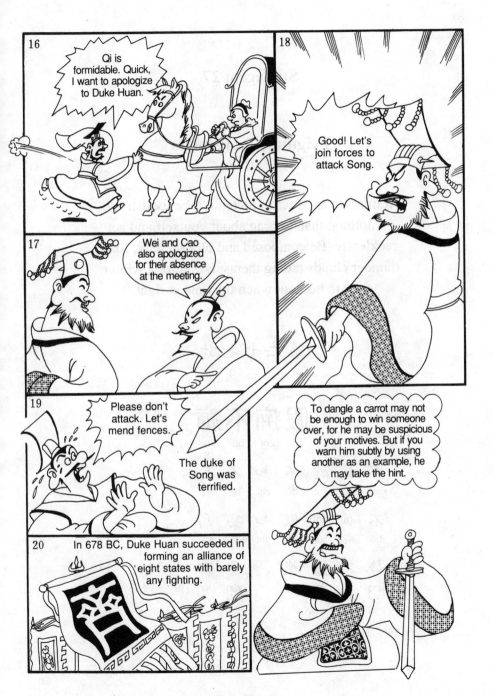

171

Stratagem 27

Feigning foolishness

At times, it is better to pretend to be foolish and do nothing than to brag about yourself and act recklessly. Be composed and plot secretly, like thunder clouds hiding themselves during winter only to bolt out when the time is right.

第二十七計
dì èr shí qī jì

假痴不癲
jiǎ chī bù diān

寧 偽 作 不 知 不 爲 ，
níng wěi zuò bù zhī bù wéi

不 偽 作 假 知 妄 爲 。
bù wěi zuò jiǎ zhī wàng wéi

静 不 露 機 ， 雲 雷 屯 也 。
jìng bù lù jī yún léi tún yě

Feigning foolishness

5 In the year AD 239, the young prince of Wei was enthroned as king for his father was critically ill. However the real power was shared between Sima Yi and Cao Shuang.

6 Cao Shuang managed to deprive Sima Yi of his military power.

7 Sima Yi feigned illness and didn't attend court. His sons Sima Shi and Sima Zhao also quit their posts to avoid suspicion.

8 Keep tabs on court affairs secretly. Bide our time.

9 During the winter of 248, Cao Shuang's henchman Li Sheng was appointed governor of Jinzhou.

175

177

26 On the fifth day of the second month in the year AD 249, Sima Yi and his sons staged a coup while Cao Shuang left the capital with the emperor to visit the imperial tombs.

27 On the ninth day of the second month, Sima Yi had Cao Shuang and his henchmen executed on charges of conspiracy.

28 Secrecy begets success, openness begets failure.

In military conflicts, it's better to conceal than to reveal moves, to play dumb than to act smart.

Stratagem 28

Remove the ladder after
the ascent

Expose your weak points deliberately to entice the
enemy to penetrate into your line, then ensnare him
in a death trap by cutting off his rearguard support.
The enemy will meet his doom because of his
misjudgement.

第二十八計

dì èr shí bā jì

上屋抽梯

shàng wū chōu tī

假 之 以 便 ， 唆 之 使 前 ，
jiǎ zhī yǐ biàn suō zhī shǐ qián

斷 其 援 應 ， 陷 之 死 地 。
duàn qí huǎn yìng xiàn zhī sǐ dì

遇 毒 ， 位 不 當 也 。
yù dú wèi bù dāng yě

Remove the ladder after the ascent

Oh! What a tough piece of preserved meat.

To crave for unrighteous gains will get you into trouble.

In battle, the "ladder" refers to deliberately exposing a weak spot to entice the enemy to advance towards you.

183

Stratagem 29

Putting fake blossoms on the tree

Use deceptive appearances to make your troop formation look much more powerful than it really is. When wild geese soar high above, the grandness of their formation is greatly enhanced by the display of their outstretched wings.

第二十九計

dì èr shí jiǔ jì

樹上開花

shù shàng kāi huā

借 局 布 勢 ， 力 小 勢 大 。

jiè jú bù shì　 lì xiǎo shì dà

鴻 漸 於 陸 ，

hóng jiàn yú lù

其 羽 可 用 爲 儀 也 。

qí yǔ kě yòng wéi yí yě

Putting fake blossoms on the tree

1. Use battle formations to fool the enemy into thinking that you're more powerful than you really are. Though weak, appear strong.

2. For instance, although originally there are no flowers on a tree...

3. Put silk flowers on it.

4. Wow! It looks real!

5 The geese soaring with outstretched wings in formation is an impressive sight. In military contexts, mere outward appearance can sometimes produce concrete effects.

6 During the Warring States period, Yan joined forces with Qin, Han, Zhao and Wei to attack Qi. More than seventy cities in Qi fell.

7 Only two cities still held out for three years: Lu, where the king of Yan was staying, and Jimo under the command of the resourceful Tian Dan.

8 He collected a quantity of gold and sent it to the Yan general Qi Jie.

Jimo is about to yield. Please don't seize our wives and concubines.

9 The Yan soldiers were overjoyed.

Going home soon.

Great!

10 The Yan troops became sluggish. Tian Dan began gathering more than a thousand bulls in the city. He covered them with purple silk and painted fantastic stripes of various colours.

11 Daggers were fixed on the horns of the bulls.

12 He fastened oil-soaked straws on the animals' tails.

13 That night, several breaches in the city walls were made.

14 The straws on the bulls' tails were lit and the raging animals charged out of the city.

15
5,000 soldiers followed behind.

16
The Yan troops panicked.

Strange beasts!

Run!

17
Meanwhile, there rose from the city a deafening racket that shook heaven and earth.

18
Qi Jie was killed.

19
Before long, Qi recovered the other cities and became a military power in the region.

Deceptive appearances coupled with unusual noises can make up for the lack of military might to subdue the enemy.

Stratagem 30

Host and guest reversed

Whenever there is a chance, enter into the
decision-making body of your ally and extend
your influence skilfully step by step. Eventually,
put it under your control.

第三十計
dì sān shí jì

反客爲主
fǎn kè wéi zhǔ

乘 隙 插 足 ， 扼 其 主 機 ，
chèng xì chā zú è qí zhǔ jī

漸 之 進 也 。
jiàn zhī jìn yě

Host and guest reversed

1 To be ordered about is to be a slave. To be esteemed is to be a guest.

2 One can either be a short-term or a long-term guest. A guest who's incompetent at doing things is a low-class guest compared to one who gradually extends his influence.

Farewell!

3 Steps for a guest to become host: One, be a guest. Two, seize opportunities. Three, have a say in things. Four, secure power. Five, take over.

Stratagems
for Desperate Situations

- **Beauty trap**
- **Empty city ploy**
- **Sow discord in the enemy's camp**
- **Inflict injury on oneself to win the enemy's trust**
- **Interlocking stratagems**
- **When retreat is the best option**

- 美人計
- 空城計
- 反間計
- 苦肉計
- 連環計
- 走爲上計

Stratagem 31

Beauty trap

When faced with a formidable enemy, try to
subdue their leader. When dealing with an able and
resourceful commander, exploit his indulgence of
sensual pleasures in order to weaken his fighting
spirit. When the commander becomes inept, his
soldiers will be demoralized, and their combat
power will be greatly weakened. This stratagem
takes advantage of the enemy's weakness
for the sake of self-protection.

第三十一計

dì sān shí yī jì

美人計

měi rén jì

兵 强 者 ， 攻 其 將 ；

bīng qiáng zhě gōng qí jiàng

將 智 者 ， 伐 其 情 。

jiàng zhì zhě fá qí qíng

將 弱 兵 頹 ， 其 勢 自 萎 。

jiàng luò bīng tuí qí shì zì wěi

利 用 禦 寇 ， 順 相 保 也 。

lì yòng yù kòu shùn xiàng bǎo yě

Beauty trap

1. When dealing with a strong enemy, try to subdue their general. Make him lose the will to lead troops into battle.

2. When the general becomes inept and the soldiers listless, their fighting ability will decline.

3.

Exploit the enemy's weakness to manipulate the enemy and create rifts so that your strength is preserved.

199

4 In the year AD 189, Han Emperor Ling Di died and Emperor Shao Di replaced him. Dong Zhuo deposed Emperor Shao Di and put Emperor Xian Di, a child, on the throne. He forced the puppet emperor to appoint him as top imperial adviser and held power with the backing of Lu Bu, the mightiest warrior of the time.

5 Court official Wang Yun wanted to get rid of Dong Zhuo.

Both of them are lustful. I'll exploit their weakness.

6 He told his sing-song girl Diao Chan, a great beauty.

We've no peace because of Dong Zhuo. Help me.

7 For the good of all, I will.

8 General Lu Bu, this is my daughter Diao Chan. I can present her to you as a concubine.

Stratagem 32

Empty city ploy

In spite of the inferiority of your forces, deliberately
make your defensive line defenceless in order
to confuse the enemy. In situations when the
enemies are many and you are few, this tactic
seems all the more intriguing.

第三十二計
dì sān shí èr jì

空城計
kōng chéng jì

虛 者 虛 之 ， 疑 中 生 疑 ；
xū zhě xū zhī yí zhōng shēng yí

剛 柔 之 際 ， 奇 而 復 奇 。
gāng róu zhī jì qí ér fù qí

Empty city ploy

1 When your military strength is nil, deliberately appear vulnerable. The enemy will be left guessing what you're up to.

2 When the enemy is strong and you're weak, this stratagem is all the more intriguing.

3 In the year 727, the Tufan army, ancestors of modern Tibetans, invaded Tang China and stormed the cities of Guazhou and Yumen before sweeping south.

4 Tang general Zhang Shougui led 5,000 troops to save Guazhou.

206

Stratagem 33

Sow discord in the enemy's camp

Spying is the best of all the deceptive measures against the enemy. Use the enemy's spies to work for you and you will win without any loss inflicted on your side.

第三十三計

dì sān shí sān jì

反間計

fǎn jiān jì

疑　中　之　疑　。　比　之　自　内　，

yí zhōng zhī yí   bǐ zhī zì nèi

不　自　失　也　。

bù zì shī yě

Sow discord in the enemy's camp

1 Among the ways of deceiving the enemy is plunging him into a fog. Induce the enemy's spies to work for you. They do all the work and you preserve your strength to achieve victory.

2 When two armies fight, the enemy will definitely send spies to gauge your strength. Turn the tables on the enemy by getting the spies to serve you.

3 Pretend to be unaware of the spies' activities and deliberately leak false information to them.

212

Stratagem 34

Inflict injury on oneself to win the enemy's trust

People rarely inflict injuries on themselves, so when they get injured, it is usually genuine. Exploit this naivety and make the enemy believe one's words; then the trick to sow discord among enemies will pay off. In this case, one takes advantage of the enemy's weakness, and makes the enemy look as if he were a naive child easily taken in.

第三十四計

dì sān shí sì jì

苦肉計

kǔ ròu jì

人 不 自 害 ，　　受 害 必 真 ；
rén bù zì hài　　shòu hài bì zhēn

假 真 真 假 ，　　間 以 得 行 。
jiǎ zhēn zhēn jiǎ　　jiān yǐ dé xíng

童 蒙 之 吉 ，　　順 以 巽 也 。
tóng méng zhī jí　　shùn yǐ xùn yě

Inflict injury on oneself to win the enemy's trust

1 People normally don't inflict injuries on themselves. When they get injured, it is usually a genuine case.

2 When the enemy believes that the spy's injury is non-deliberate, the stratagem can work. The spy can then carry out his mission without the enemy suspecting anything.

3 Injuring oneself goes against conventional wisdom. But its aim is to fool the enemy to achieve your goals.

4 This stratagem is often used together with Stratagem 33. Pretend to take no notice of being monitored and feed the enemy with information which he won't suspect is false.

5 During the Spring and Autumn period, King He Lu wanted to assassinate the prince of Wei, Qing Ji.

6 His adviser Wu Zixu said:

Qing Ji is a powerfully-built man. To kill him we must call upon Yao Li.

7 Yao Li deliberately insulted He Lu in front of others.

Chop off his right hand!

8

9

10 Yao Li went to seek refuge in Qing Ji's domain.

215

216

Stratagem 35

Interlocking stratagems

When the enemy possesses a superior force, do not
attack recklessly. Instead, weaken him by
devising plots to bring him into a difficult position
of his own doing. Good leadership plays a key role
in winning a war. A wise commander gains
Heaven's favour.

第三十五計

dì sān shí wǔ jì

連環計

lián huán jì

將	多	兵	眾	，	不	可	以	敵	，
jiàng	duō	bīng	zhòng		bù	kě	yǐ	dí	

使	其	自	纍	，	以	殺	其	勢	。
shǐ	qí	zì	lèi		yǐ	shā	qí	shì	

在	師	中	吉	，	承	天	寵	也	。
zài	shī	zhōng	jí		chéng	tiān	chǒng	yě	

1 If the enemy has superior strength, don't be foolhardy and engage them in battle. Instead, think of a way to entangle them for this will weaken them.

2

For a strategist who can pull off his plan brilliantly to overcome the enemy, it's like receiving divine help.

3 In the late Spring and Autumn period, the chief minister of Qi, Tian Chang, instigated Duke Jian to destroy the state of Lu for he wanted to usurp power.

4 In order to save his home state, Confucius despatched his most eloquent disciple Zi Gong to Qi to dissuade Qi from attacking Lu.

222

27 If Wu wins, it might turn on Lu. I need to borrow Jin's influence to discourage Wu.

28 Zi Gong thus proceeded to meet Duke Ding of Jin.

After defeating Qi, Wu will challenge Jin for dominance.

29 Resist Wu.

30 In the year 484 BC, Fu Chai led the forces of Wu, Yue and Lu to crush Qi.

31 Fu Chai's next target was Jin. But Jin was well-prepared and Fu Chai couldn't realize his ambition.

Although this stratagem has many uses, the aim is to be the overall winner. Exploit the key weaknesses of your opponents to hobble them and prevent them from acting effectively against you.

Stratagem 36

When retreat is the best option

To avoid combat with a powerful enemy, the
whole army should retreat and wait for the right
time to advance again. This is not inconsistent
with normal military principles.

第三十六計

dì sān shí liù jì

走爲上計

zhǒu wéi shàng jì

全 師 避 敵 。 左 次 無 咎 ,

quán shī bì dí zuǒ cì wú jiù

未 失 常 也 。

wèi shī cháng yě

When retreat is the best option

229

A Brief Chronology of Chinese History

夏 Xia Dynasty			About 2100 – 1600 BC
商 Shang Dynasty			About 1600 – 1100 BC
周 Zhou Dynasty	西周 Western Zhou Dynasty		About 1100 – 771 BC
	東周 Eastern Zhou Dynasty		770 – 256 BC
	春秋 Spring and Autumn Period		770 – 476 BC
	戰國 Warring States		475 – 221 BC
秦 Qin Dynasty			221 – 207 BC
漢 Han Dynasty	西漢 Western Han		206 BC – AD 24
	東漢 Eastern Han		25 – 220
三國 Three Kingdoms	魏 Wei		220 – 265
	蜀漢 Shu Han		221 – 263
	吳 Wu		222 – 280
西晉 Western Jin Dynasty			265 – 316
東晉 Eastern Jin Dynasty			317 – 420
南北朝 Northern and Southern Dynasties	南朝 Southern Dynasties	宋 Song	420 – 479
		齊 Qi	479 – 502
		梁 Liang	502 – 557
		陳 Chen	557 – 589
	北朝 Northern Dynasties	北魏 Northern Wei	386 – 534
		東魏 Eastern Wei	534 – 550
		北齊 Northern Qi	550 – 577
		西魏 Western Wei	535 – 556
		北周 Northern Zhou	557 – 581
隋 Sui Dynasty			581 – 618
唐 Tang Dynasty			618 – 907
五代 Five Dynasties	後梁 Later Liang		907 – 923
	後唐 Later Tang		923 – 936
	後晉 Later Jin		936 – 946
	後漢 Later Han		947 – 950
	後周 Later Zhou		951 – 960
宋 Song Dynasty	北宋 Northern Song Dynasty		960 – 1127
	南宋 Southern Song Dynasty		1127 – 1279
遼 Liao Dynasty			916 – 1125
金 Jin Dynasty			1115 – 1234
元 Yuan Dynasty			1271 – 1368
明 Ming Dynasty			1368 – 1644
清 Qing Dynasty			1644 – 1911
中華民國 Republic of China			1912 – 1949
中華人民共和國 People's Republic of China			1949 –

Strategy & Leadership Series by Wang Xuanming

Thirty-six Stratagems: Secret Art of War
Translated by Koh Kok Kiang (cartoons) &
Liu Yi (text of the stratagems)
   A Chinese military classic which emphasizes deceptive schemes to achieve military objectives. It has attracted the attention of military authorities and general readers alike.

Six Strategies for War: The Practice of Effective Leadership
Translated by Alan Chong
   A powerful book for rulers, administrators and leaders, it covers critical areas in management and warfare including: how to recruit talents and manage the state; how to beat the enemy and build an empire; how to lead wisely; and how to manoeuvre brilliantly.

Gems of Chinese Wisdom: Mastering the Art of Leadership
Translated by Leong Weng Kam
   Wise up with this delightful collection of tales and anecdotes on the wisdom of great men and women in Chinese history, including Confucius, Meng Changjun and Gou Jian.

Three Strategies of Huang Shi Gong: The Art of Government
Translated by Alan Chong
   Reputedly one of man's oldest monograph on military strategy, it unmasks the secrets behind brilliant military manoeuvres, clever deployment and control of subordinates, and effective government.

100 Strategies of War: Brilliant Tactics in Action
Translated by Yeo Ai Hoon
   The book captures the essence of extensive military knowledge and practice, and explores the use of psychology in warfare, the importance of building diplomatic relations with the enemy's neighbours, the use of espionage and reconnaissance, etc.

Latest Titles in
Strategy & Leadership Series

Chinese Business Strategies

The Chinese are known for being shrewd businessmen able to thrive under the toughest market conditions. The secret of their success lies in 10 time-tested principles of Chinese entrepreneurship.

This book offers readers 30 real-life, ancient case studies with comments on their application in the context of modern business.

Sixteen Strategies of Zhuge Liang

Zhuge Liang, the legendary statesman and military commander during the Three Kingdoms Period, is the epitome of wisdom.

Well-grounded in military principles of Sun Zi and other masters before him, he excelled in applying them in state administration and his own innovations, thus winning many spectacular victories with his uncanny anticipation of enemy moves.

CHINESE HERITAGE SERIES
Capture the essence of Chinese culture in comics

Enjoy 10% discount and free postage.

Title	Qty	*Price S$	Total
Origins of Chinese Festivals		$14.74	$
Chinese Code of Success: Maxims by Zhu Zi		$14.74	$
Sunzi's Art of War		$14.74	$
Principles of Feng Shui		$12.51	$
Complete Analects of Confucius Vol 1		$17.61	$
Complete Analects of Confucius Vol 2		$17.61	$
Complete Analects of Confucius Vol 3		$17.61	$

Prices indicated after 10% discount (GST inclusive)
Offer is for readers in Singapore only.

Send this complete page for your mail order

I wish to purchase the above-mentioned titles at the nett price of S$ _____

Enclosed is my postal order/money order/cheque/ for S$ _____ (No.: _____)

Name (Mr/Mrs/Ms) _____ Tel _____

Address _____

_____ Fax _____

Please charge the amount of S$ _____ to my VISA/MASTER CARD account (only

Visa/Master Card accepted)

Card No. _____ Card Expiry Date _____

Card Holder's Name (Mr/Mrs/Ms) _____ Signature _____

Send to: ASIAPAC BOOKS PTE LTD 996 Bendemeer Road #06-08/09 Kallang Basin
Industrial Estate Singapore 339944 Tel: (65)3928455 Fax: (65)3926455

Prices are subject to change without prior notice.

⊞ RETURN OF THE ⊞
CONDOR HEROES

神 雕 侠 侣

Subscription Form

Bestselling martial-art comics by Louis Cha
Illustrated by Wee Tian Beng

Per Issue
Usual: S$8.76
Now: S$7.70
(local order)

Now in 18 volumes, published bimonthly. Subscribe now and enjoy special discounts.

I wish to subscribe for *Return of the Condor Heroes Series* from Volume ____ to Volume ____.

❏ Singapore Order: Nett price of S$7.70 per volume (free postage)

❏ Overseas Order: Nett price of S$10.20 per volume (inclusive of postage by surface mail)

Enclosed is my postal order/money order/cheque/ for S$_____ (No.: _____)

Name (Mr/Mrs/Ms) _____ Tel _____

Address _____

_____ Fax _____

Please charge the amount of S$ _____ to my VISA/MASTER CARD account (only Visa/Master Card accepted)

Card No. _____ Card Expiry Date _____

Card Holder's Name (Mr/Mrs/Ms) _____ Signature _____

Send to: ASIAPAC BOOKS PTE LTD 996 Bendemeer Road #06-08/09 Kallang Basin
Industrial Estate Singapore 339944 Tel: (65)3928455 Fax: (65)3926455

Note: Prices subject to change without prior notice. Each issue to be mailed to you upon publication — one volume every two months.

《亞太漫畫系列》

智謀叢書

三十六計

編著: 王宣銘

翻譯: 許國强

劉毅

亞太圖書（新）有限公司出版